SRA
ART
Connections

Assessment

D1501143

Columbus, OH

The McGraw·Hill Companies

SRAonline.com

Send all inquiries to:
SRA/McGraw-Hill
8787 Orion Place
Columbus, OH 43240-4027

Printed in the United States of America.

ISBN 0-07-601865-2

1 2 3 4 5 6 7 8 9 MAZ 10 09 08 07 06 05 04

The McGraw-Hill Companies

Table of Contents

Unit 5 Proportion, Distortion, and Scale

Unit 6 Variety, Harmony, and Unity

Assessment in Art

"Assessment provides the basis for schools to be accountable to their communities for student learning in all subjects. As such, assessment is also an important part of a good art education. Assessment occurs during as well as after the art lesson. It provides some assurance that students are learning what teachers intend to teach."

—Carmen L. Armstrong

Designing Assessment in Art. National Art Education Association, 1994

Quality art programs require students to engage in problem solving, visual discrimination, and critical and creative thinking processes. These processes include visual memory, communication, comparing and contrasting, predicting, hypothesizing, and evaluating. Art education teaches key concepts and skills such as shape, color recognition, size differentiation, letter and number recognition, listening skills, sequencing, following directions, hand-eye and motor coordination, kinesthetic and spatial relationships, and direction and location. A valid assessment of an art program can demonstrate that students are, in fact, developing these essential skills.

There are a variety of *Art Connections* assessment tools available to art educators.

- **Blackline master assessments** in this book evaluate a student's understanding of the elements and principles of art presented in each lesson of the *Art Connections* program. There are 36 English and Spanish blackline master assessments, one for each lesson. These assessments can be used individually, following each lesson, or they can be grouped and used two or three times during a unit.

- **Evaluation Checklists** for Art History and Culture, Art Criticism, Aesthetic Perception, Creative Expression, and Portfolio Assessment presented on the following pages are intended to be flexible so that teachers can adjust them to various classroom and individual needs. These checklists can be used at the teacher's discretion. They are intended to be copied for each evaluation and may be kept in each student's art portfolio. Each accomplishment on the Evaluation Checklists is designed to be rated on a three-point scale.

    3—Established. The student's response or work demonstrates understanding and competence.
    2—Emerging. The student demonstrates some degree of knowledge and skill.
    1—Not yet. There is not yet evidence in the student's work that he or she has grasped the skill.

- **Creative Expression** rubrics provide valuable guidance for assessing the artwork that students create in class. There are 36 Creative Expression rubrics, one for each lesson in the *Art Connections* program.

Evaluation Checklists

Art History and Culture

Accomplishment	Not Applicable	Not Yet 1	Emerging 2	Established 3	Notes
Compares and contrasts artwork by different artists					
Recognizes artist's culture					
Recognizes artist's style					
Identifies artwork's place of origin					
Identifies artist's work					
Identifies subject matter of artwork					
Identifies cultural symbols in artwork					
Understands that art is practiced by all cultures, past and present					
Identifies time period of artwork					
Uses appropriate art vocabulary in describing, interpreting, or reflecting on artwork					

Art Criticism

Accomplishment	Not Applicable	Not Yet 1	Emerging 2	Established 3	Notes
Describes the elements and principles of art used in a work					
Analyzes artwork effectively					
Interprets the meaning and purpose of artwork					
Judges artwork according to specific criteria					
Uses appropriate art vocabulary in describing, interpreting, or reflecting on artwork					
Identifies a variety of art career opportunities					
Recognizes artist's purpose or main idea of the work					
Supports analysis, interpretation, and judgments with examples					

Evaluation Checklists

Aesthetic Perception

Accomplishment	Not Applicable	Not Yet 1	Emerging 2	Established 3	Notes
Describes the multisensory characteristics in a work of art					
Uses appropriate art vocabulary in describing, interpreting, or reflecting on artwork					
Recognizes connections between art and other disciplines					
Compares and contrasts visual characteristics of objects and subjects					
Recognizes similarities and differences between visual art and music, dance, and theatre					
Demonstrates ability to observe elements and principles of art in the environment					
Draws appropriate conclusions based on aesthetic perception					

Creative Expression

Accomplishment	Not Applicable	Not Yet 1	Emerging 2	Established 3	Notes
Knows the differences between materials, techniques, and processes					
Uses different media, techniques, and processes to communicate ideas, experiences, and stories					
Uses art materials and tools in a safe and responsible manner					
Understands and effectively uses the elements and principles of art to communicate ideas					
Creates original, imaginative, and inventive works of art in 2-D and 3-D					
Demonstrates skill and craftsmanship					

Evaluation Checklists

Portfolio Assessment

Accomplishment	Not Applicable	Not Yet 1	Emerging 2	Established 3	Notes
Completeness: Artwork in portfolio meets assigned requirements					
Effort: Artwork demonstrates concerted effort					
Variety: Artwork in portfolio demonstrates a variety of media, techniques, and processes					
Skill: Artwork demonstrates ability to utilize elements and principles of art to communicate ideas					
Volume: Portfolio includes a sufficient amount of work					
Quality: Artwork demonstrates appropriate level of quality					
Risk-Taking: Artwork demonstrates taking risks in creating/choosing works that go beyond minimum expectations					
Growth: Artwork demonstrates improvement					
Self-Evaluation: Student shows awareness of strengths and weaknesses					

Line and Qualities of Line

A. Matching

Match the words in Column 1 to the definitions in Column 2.

Column 1

Column 2

_____ **1.** curved

a. lines that move up and down

_____ **2.** horizontal

b. lines that move from side to side

_____ **3.** zigzag

c. lines that move on a slant

_____ **4.** vertical

d. lines that are made by joining diagonal lines

_____ **5.** diagonal

e. lines that bend and change gradually or form spirals

B. Drawing

Draw and label each one of the five lines.

_____   _____   _____   _____   _____

C. Writing

Examine *Ceremonial Skirt* and *Plate 24.* Write a paragraph about what type of line is used most often.

La línea y las cualidades de la línea

A. Emparejar

Empareja las palabras de la columna 1 con las definiciones de la columna 2.

Columna 1

_____ **1.** curva

_____ **2.** horizontal

_____ **3.** en zigzag

_____ **4.** vertical

_____ **5.** diagonal

Columna 2

a. líneas que se mueven hacia arriba y hacia abajo

b. líneas que se mueven de lado a lado

c. líneas que se mueven en un plano inclinado

d. líneas que se forman al unir líneas diagonales

e. líneas que se doblan y cambian gradualmente o forman espirales

B. Dibujar

Dibuja y rotula cada una de las cinco líneas.

_____ _____ _____ _____

C. Escribir

Examina las obras *Ceremonial Skirt* y *Plate 24*. Escribe un párrafo acerca del tipo de línea que se usa más a menudo.

Geometric and Free-Form Shapes

A. Matching

Match the words in Column 1 to the definitions in Column 2.

Column 1

_____ **1.** geometric shapes

_____ **2.** free-form shapes

_____ **3.** complex geometric shape

_____ **4.** shape

Column 2

a. a combination of geometric shapes

b. are exact and have mathematical measurements

c. are irregular or uneven

d. two-dimensional area measured by height and width

B. Drawing

Draw and label three geometric shapes and two free-form shapes.

_____ _____ _____ _____ _____

C. Writing

Examine the shapes in the quilt created by Harriet Powers. Write a paragraph about the free-form shapes that are repeated.

_____

_____

_____

Figuras geométricas y abstractas

A. Emparejar

Empareja las palabras de la columna 1 con las definiciones de la columna 2.

Columna 1

_____ **1.** figuras geométricas

_____ **2.** figuras abstractas

_____ **3.** figura geométrica compleja

_____ **4.** figura

Columna 2

a. una combinación de figuras geométricas

b. son exactas y tienen medidas matemáticas

c. son irregulares o desiguales

d. área bidimensional que se mide por el alto y el ancho

B. Dibujar

Dibuja y rotula tres figuras geométricas y dos figuras abstractas.

_____ _____ _____ _____ _____

C. Escribir

Examina las figuras en la colcha creada por Harriet Powers. Escribe un párrafo acerca de las figuras abstractas que se repiten.

Geometric Forms

A. Short Answer

Complete each sentence.

1. A form is _____.

2. Geometric forms _____.

B. Drawing

Draw and label three geometric forms.

_____ _____ _____

C. Writing

Look at the sculpture *Cubi XVII*. Write a paragraph that describes the shapes used in *Cubi XVII*.

_____

_____

_____

_____

_____

_____

_____

_____

Formas geométricas

A. Respuesta corta

Completa cada frase.

1. Una forma es _____.

2. Las formas geométricas _____.

B. Dibujar

Dibuja y rotula tres formas geométricas.

_____   _____   _____

C. Escribir

Mira la escultura *Cubi XVII*. Escribe un párrafo que describa las figuras que se usaron en *Cubi XVII*.

_____
_____
_____
_____
_____
_____
_____
_____

Free-Form Forms

A. Short Answer

Complete each sentence.

1. A free-form form is _____ .

2. A free-form form is also called a _____ .

B. Drawing

Draw and label three free-form forms.

_____ _____ _____

C. Writing

Look at the sculpture by Paul Baliker. Write a paragraph that describes the forms used in *Fish Story*.

Formas abstractas

A. Respuesta corta

Completa cada frase.

1. Una forma abstracta es _____.

2. A una forma abstracta también se le llama _____.

B. Dibujar

Dibuja y rotula tres formas abstractas.

_____   _____   _____

C. Escribir

Mira la escultura de Paul Baliker. Escribe un párrafo que describa
las formas usadas en la *Fish Story*.

Space and Perspective

A. Matching

Match the words in Column 1 to the definitions in Column 2

Column 1

Column 2

_____ **1.** perspective

a. objects that are closer look larger than objects that are farther away

_____ **2.** overlapping

b. creates the illusion of depth on a flat surface

_____ **3.** size

c. one object covers a portion of another object

_____ **4.** placement

d. objects placed lower in the picture appear to be closer than those placed near eye level

B. Drawing

Make a drawing using three perspective techniques.

C. Writing

Look at the paintings by Pannini and van Gogh. Write a paragraph about the overlapping in both paintings.

El espacio y la perspectiva

A. Emparejar

Empareja las palabras de la columna 1 con las definiciones de la columna 2.

Columna 1

_____ **1.** perspectiva

_____ **2.** superponer

_____ **3.** tamaño

_____ **4.** colocación

Columna 2

a. los objetos más cercanos se ven más grandes que los objetos lejanos

b. crea la ilusión de profundidad en una superficie plana

c. un objeto cubre parte de otro

d. los objetos que se colocan más abajo en la pintura parecen estar más cerca que los que se colocan a nivel de la vista

B. Dibujar

Haz un dibujo usando tres técnicas de perspectiva.

C. Escribir

Mira las pinturas de Pannini y van Gogh. Escribe un párrafo acerca de la superposición en ambas pinturas.

Positive and Negative Space

A. Short Answer

Complete each sentence.

1. Space is _____.

2. In two- and three-dimensional art, positive space is _____.

3. Negative space is _____.

B. Drawing

Draw an example of positive and negative space.

C. Writing

Look at the sculptures *Proposal for a Monument to Apollinaire* and *Seated Man #4.* In a paragraph, describe the negative space.

El espacio positivo y negativo

A. Respuesta corta

Completa cada frase.

1. El espacio es _____.

2. En el arte bidimensional y tridimensional, el espacio positivo es _____.

3. El espacio negativo es _____.

B. Dibujar

Dibuja un ejemplo de espacio positivo y negativo.

C. Escribir

Mira las esculturas *Proposal for a Monument to Apollinaire* y *Seated Man #4.* En un párrafo, describe el espacio negativo.

Hue

A. Matching

Match the words in Column 1 to the definitions in Column 2.

Column 1   **Column 2**

_____ **1.** hue   **a.** red, yellow, and blue

_____ **2.** color spectrum **b.** when light bends and separates into colors

_____ **3.** primary hue   **c.** the mixture of two primary hues

_____ **4.** secondary hue   **d.** the mixture of a primary hue and a secondary hue

_____ **5.** intermediate hue **e.** another name for *color*

B. Short Answer

Label each color as primary or secondary.

1. red   _____

2. orange   _____

3. violet   _____

4. yellow   _____

C. Writing

Look at *Anna and David* and *Conception Synchromy*. Write a paragraph about the colors in both pieces of artwork.

_____

_____

_____

_____

_____

El matiz

A. Emparejar

Empareja las palabras de la columna 1 con las definiciones de la columna 2.

Columna 1

_____ **1.** matiz

_____ **2.** espectro del color

_____ **3.** matiz primario

_____ **4.** matiz secundario

_____ **5.** matiz intermedio

Columna 2

a. rojo, amarillo y azul

b. cuando se dobla la luz y se descompone en colores

c. la mezcla de dos matices primarios

d. la mezcla de un matiz primario y uno secundario

e. otro nombre para *color*

B. Respuesta corta

Rotula cada color como primario o secundario.

1. rojo _____

2. anaranjado _____

3. violeta _____

4. amarillo _____

C. Escribir

Mira las obras *Anna and David* y *Conception Synchromy*. Escribe un párrafo acerca de los colores en ambas obras de arte.

_____

_____

_____

_____

_____

Value

A. Matching

Match the words in Column 1 to the definitions in Column 2.

Column 1

_____ **1.** tint

_____ **2.** shade

_____ **3.** hatching

_____ **4.** cross-hatching

_____ **5.** blending

_____ **6.** stippling

Column 2

a. a light value of a hue

b. a shading technique that is a series of parallel lines

c. a shading technique that is a gradual change from light to dark or dark to light

d. a dark value of a hue

e. a shading technique where sets of parallel lines cross

f. a shading technique that uses dots

B. Drawing

Draw and label three shading techniques.

_____ _____ _____

C. Writing

Find the light and dark areas in *Snow Scene*. Write a paragraph about these areas.

_____

_____

_____

El valor

A. Emparejar

Empareja las palabras de la columna 1 con las definiciones de la columna 2.

Columna 1

_____ **1.** tinte

_____ **2.** tono

_____ **3.** sombreado con rayas

_____ **4.** sombreado con rayas entrecruzadas

_____ **5.** mezclado

_____ **6.** punteado

Columna 2

a. a un valor claro de un matiz

b. una técnica de sombreado con una serie de líneas paralelas

c. una técnica de sombreado con un cambio gradual de claro a oscuro o de oscuro a claro

d. un valor oscuro de un matiz

e. una técnica de sombreado en que se cruzan conjuntos de líneas paralelas

f. una técnica de sombreado en que se usan puntos

B. Dibujar

Dibuja y rotula tres técnicas de sombreado.

_____ _____ _____

C. Escribir

Busca las áreas claras y oscuras en la *Snow Scene.* Escribe un párrafo acerca de estas áreas.

_____

_____

Intensity

A. Short Answer

Complete each sentence.

1. Intensity is _____ .

2. Complementary colors are _____ .

B. Short Answer

Write the answers to the question.
What are the complementary colors for each of the following?

1. red _____

2. blue _____

3. yellow _____

C. Writing

Examine the colors in *Portrait of a Young Girl in Black*. Write a
paragraph about why you think Derain used these colors.

_____

_____

_____

_____

_____

_____

_____

_____

_____

La intensidad

A. Respuesta corta

Completa cada frase.

1. La intensidad es _____.

2. Los colores complementarios son _____.

B. Respuesta corta

Escribe las respuestas a la pregunta.
¿Cuáles son los colores complementarios para cada uno de los siguientes colores?

1. rojo _____

2. azul _____

3. amarillo _____

C. Escribir

Examina los colores en el *Portrait of a Young Girl in Black*. Escribe un párrafo acerca de por qué crees que Derain usó estos colores.

Color Schemes

A. Matching

Match the words in Column 1 to the definitions in Column 2.

Column 1

_____ **1.** color scheme

_____ **2.** analogous colors

_____ **3.** warm colors

_____ **4.** cool colors

Column 2

a. colors like red, yellow, and orange

b. colors like violet, blue, and green that

c. a plan for organizing the colors used in an artwork

d. colors that sit side by side on the color wheel and have a common hue

B. Drawing

Choose two sets of analogous colors. Paint and label them in the boxes.

_____   _____

C. Writing

Look at the paintings *Fishing Boats* and *Fireworks.* Write a paragraph about which colors catch your attention first.

_____

_____

_____

_____

Los esquemas de color

A. Emparejar

Empareja las palabras de la columna 1 con las definiciones de la columna 2.

Columna 1

_____ **1.** esquema de color

_____ **2.** colores análogos

_____ **3.** colores cálidos

_____ **4.** colores fríos

Columna 2

a. colores como rojo, amarillo y anaranjado

b. colores como violeta, azul y verde

c. un plan para organizar los colores usados en una obra de arte

d. colores que están uno al lado del otro en el círculo cromático y que tienen un matiz en común

B. Dibujar

Escoge dos series de colores análogos. Pinta y rotula los cuadros con estos colores.

_____ _____ _____

C. Escribir

Mira las pinturas *Fishing Boats* y *Fireworks*. Escribe un párrafo acerca de cuáles colores captan primero tu atención.

_____

_____

_____

_____

Visual Texture

A. Matching

Match the words in Column 1 to the definitions in Column 2.

Column 1

_____ **1.** texture

_____ **2.** visual texture

_____ **3.** simulated texture

Column 2

a. the illusion of a three-dimensional surface

b. a texture that imitates real textures

c. how things feel or look as if they might feel if touched

B. Short Answer

List an object for each texture.

1. rough _____

2. smooth _____

3. shiny _____

4. matte _____

C. Writing

Look at the work *Two Birds in Hand.* Write a paragraph about which areas in the picture look rough.

_____

_____

_____

_____

_____

_____

_____

La textura visual

A. Emparejar

Empareja las palabras de la columna 1 con las definiciones de la
columna 2.

Columna 1

_____ **1.** textura

_____ **2.** textura visual

_____ **3.** textura simulada

Columna 2

a. la ilusión de una superficie tridimensional

b. una textura que imita texturas verdaderas

c. cómo se sienten o se ven las cosas como se sentirían si
se tocaran

B. Respuesta corta

Alista un objeto para cada textura.

1. áspero _____

2. suave _____

3. brillante _____

4. mate _____

C. Escribir

Mira la obra *Two Birds in Hand*. Escribe un párrafo acerca de las
áreas de la pintura que parecen ser ásperas.

_____
_____
_____
_____
_____
_____
_____

Tactile Texture

A. Short Answer

Complete each sentence.

1. A tactile texture is _____.

2. Mixed-media is _____.

B. Drawing

Draw an example of two objects that are rough and smooth.

C. Writing

Look closely at both headpieces. Write a paragraph describing how the different objects attached to the hats feel.

La textura táctil

A. Respuesta corta

Completa cada frase.

1. Una textura táctil es _____.

2. La combinación de medios es _____.

B. Dibujar

Dibuja un ejemplo de dos objetos que sean ásperos y suaves.

C. Escribir

Mira detalladamente las dos prendas para la cabeza. Escribe un párrafo que describa cómo se sienten los diferentes objetos sujetos a los sombreros.

Motif and Pattern

A **Short Answer**

Complete each sentence.

1. A motif is _____.

2. A pattern is _____.

B. **Drawing**

Draw and label a motif and a pattern.

C. **Writing**

Look at *Face Mask of Ḵumugwe'*. What repeated colors and shapes give a hint that the *Face Mask of Ḵumugwe'* was used in a dance about the ocean?

El motivo y el patrón

A. Respuesta corta

Completa cada frase.

1. Un motivo es _____ .

2. Un patrón es _____ .

B. Dibujar

Dibuja y rotula un motivo y un patrón.

C. Escribir

Mira *Face Mask of Ḵumugwe'*. ¿Qué colores y figuras que se repiten nos dan una pista de que *Face Mask of Ḵumugwe'* se usó en una danza acerca del océano?

Two-Dimensional Pattern

A. Matching

Match the words in Column 1 to the definitions in Column 2.

Column 1

_____ **1.** pattern

_____ **2.** motif

_____ **3.** random pattern

_____ **4.** regular pattern

_____ **5.** alternating pattern

Column 2

a. occurs when the motif is repeated in no apparent order

b. repeats a motif but changes position, alters spacing between motifs, or adds a second motif

c. the unit of repetition in the pattern

d. a repeated surface decoration

e. occurs when identical motifs are repeated with an equal amount of space between them

B. Drawing

Draw and label random, regular, and alternating patterns.

C. Writing

Examine *King* and *Indian Fantasy*. Write a paragraph about the colors, lines, and shapes that you recognize in both works of art.

El patrón bidimensional

A. Emparejar

Empareja las palabras de la columna 1 con las definiciones en la columna 2.

Columna 1

_____ **1.** patrón

_____ **2.** motivo

_____ **3.** patrón al azar

_____ **4.** patrón regular

_____ **5.** patrón alterno

Columna 2

a. ocurre cuando se repite el motivo sin un orden aparente

b. se repite un motivo pero se cambia la posición, se altera el espacio entre los motivos o se agrega un segundo motivo

c. la unidad de repetición en el patrón

d. un adorno de superficie repetido

e. ocurre cuando se repiten motivos idénticos con igual espacio entre ellos

B. Dibujar

Dibuja y rotula patrones al azar, regular y alterno.

C. Escribir

Examina *King* y *Indian Fantasy*. Escribe un párrafo sobre los colores, las líneas y las figuras que reconozcas en ambas obras de arte.

Three-Dimensional Pattern

A. Short Answer

Complete each sentence.

1. The three types of pattern are _____

_____.

2. Patterns can be added to all forms of sculpture by _____

_____.

B. Drawing

Draw and label two patterns that could be used on a backpack.

_____ _____

C. Writing

Look at *Carved Animals* and *Ceramic Figures.* Write a paragraph about why you think the patterns on the pieces make them interesting.

El patrón tridimensional

A. Respuesta corta

Completa cada frase.

1. Los tres tipos de patrón son _____

_____.

2. Se pueden agregar patrones a todas las formas de escultura al _____

_____.

B. Dibujar

Dibuja y rotula dos patrones que podrían usarse en una mochila.

_____   _____

C. Escribir

Mira *Carved Animals* y *Ceramic Figures*. Escribe un párrafo acerca
de por qué crees que los patrones de las obras las hacen
interesantes.

_____

_____

_____

_____

_____

_____

_____

Rhythm

A. Short Answer

Complete each sentence.

1. Rhythm is _____.

2. In a piece of art, visual rhythm is created by _____.

B. Drawing

Draw an example of visual rhythm that can be found in nature.

C. Writing

Look at *Portrait of Dora Maar.* Write a paragraph about the most important element in this work.

El ritmo

A. **Respuesta corta**

Completa cada frase.

1. El ritmo es _____.

2. En una obra de arte, el ritmo visual se crea al _____.

B. **Dibujar**

Dibuja un ejemplo de ritmo visual que puede hallarse en la naturaleza.

C. **Escribir**

Mira *Portrait of Dora Maar*. Escribe un párrafo acerca del elemento más importante en esta obra.

Visual Movement

A. Short Answer

Complete each sentence.

1. Movement is _____.

2. Artists use visual movement in a work of art by _____.

B. Short Answer

Are these examples of visual movement? Write *yes* or *no* next to
each example.

1. a clothes line with clothing of like colors _____

2. a field of like animals _____

3. a person sitting on a bench _____

4. telephone poles _____

C. Writing

Examine *Exotic Landscape* and *Bottom of the Ravine.* Are these
paintings active? Explain your answer in a paragraph.

_____
_____
_____
_____
_____
_____
_____
_____
_____
_____
_____

El movimiento visual

A. Respuesta corta

Completa cada frase.

1. El movimiento es _____ .

2. Los artistas usan movimiento visual en una obra de arte al _____ .

B. Respuesta corta

¿Éstos son ejemplos de movimiento visual? Escribe *sí* o *no* al lado
de cada ejemplo.

1. una línea de ropa con ropa de colores semejantes _____

2. un campo de animales parecidos _____

3. una persona sentada en un banco _____

4. postes telefónicos _____

C. Escribir

Examina *Exotic Landscape* y *Bottom of the Ravine.* ¿Estas pinturas
son activas? Explica tu respuesta en un párrafo.

_____
_____
_____
_____
_____
_____
_____
_____
_____
_____

Kinetic Movement

A. Matching

Match the words in Column 1 to the definitions in Column 2.

Column 1

_____ **1.** movement

_____ **2.** kinetic movement

_____ **3.** kinetic sculpture

Column 2

a. actual or real movement

b. a three-dimensional form that actually moves in space

c. the principle of art that leads a viewer's eyes through a work of art

B. Short Answer

Are these examples of kinetic movement? Write *yes* or *no* next to each example.

1. a flag waving _____

2. a book lying on a table _____

3. a mobile moving _____

4. a car waiting at a traffic light _____

C. Writing

Look at *Double Pan Swoosh.* Do you think Rose tried to capture the movement of a real object?

El movimiento cinético

A. Emparejar

Empareja las palabras de la columna 1 con las definiciones en la columna 2.

Columna 1

_____ **1.** movimiento

_____ **2.** movimiento cinético

_____ **3.** escultura cinética

Columna 2

a. movimiento verdadero o real

b. una forma tridimensional que realmente se mueve en el espacio

c. el principio artístico que guía la vista del espectador por una obra de arte

B. Respuesta corta

¿Éstos son ejemplos de movimiento cinético? Escribe *sí* o *no* al lado de cada ejemplo.

1. una bandera ondeando _____

2. un libro sobre una mesa _____

3. un móvil que se mueve _____

4. un carro esperando en un semáforo _____

C. Escribir

Mira *Double Pan Swoosh.* ¿Crees que Rose trató de captar el movimiento de un objeto real?

_____

_____

_____

_____

_____

_____

Formal Balance and Symmetry

A. Matching

Match each word in Column 1 to its definition in Column 2.

Column 1

_____ **1.** balance

_____ **2.** formal balance

_____ **3.** central axis

_____ **4.** symmetry

Column 2

a. the real or imaginary line that divides a design in half

b. the principle of design that relates to visual weight in a work of art

c. a type of formal balance in which the two halves are exactly the same

d. occurs when equal, or very similar, elements are placed on opposite sides of a central axis

B. Drawing

Draw a design that shows formal balance. Lightly draw the central axis.

C. Writing

Study the United States Capitol and write about paragraph about its symmetry.

El equilibrio formal y la simetría

A. Emparejar

Empareja cada palabra de la Columna 1 con su definición en la Columna 2.

Columna 1

_____ **1.** equilibrio

_____ **2.** equilibrio formal

_____ **3.** eje central

_____ **4.** simetría

Columna 2

a. la línea real o imaginaria que divide un diseño por la mitad

b. el principio de diseño que se relaciona con el peso visual en una obra de arte

c. un tipo de equilibrio formal en el cual dos mitades son exactamente iguales

d. ocurre cuando elementos iguales, o muy parecidos, se colocan en lados opuestos de un eje central

B. Dibujar

Dibuja un diseño eso tiene equilibrio formal. Dibuja levemente el eje central.

C. Escribir

Estudia el Capitolio de Estados Unidos y escribe un párrafo sobre su simetría.

Approximate Symmetry

A. Short Answer

Answer each question.

1. What is approximate symmetry? _____

_____

2. Why would an artist use approximate symmetry? _____

_____

B. Drawing

Sketch a still life that shows approximate symmetry.

C. Writing

Look at *James Vibert, Sculptor* and write a description about the artist's use of approximate symmetry.

La simetría aproximada

A. Respuesta corta

Contesta cada pregunta.

1. ¿Qué es la simetría aproximada? _____

_____

2. ¿Por qué un artista usaría simetría aproximada? _____

_____

B. Dibujar

Dibuja una naturaleza muestra para mostrar simetría aproximada.

C. Escribir

Mira la obra *James Vibert, Sculptor* y escribe una descripción de
cómo el artista usó la simetría aproximada.

Informal Balance

A. Matching

Match each word in Column 1 to its definition in Column 2.

Column 1

Column 2

_____ **1.** informal balance

a. a bright color has more visual weight than a dull color

_____ **2.** size

b. a large positive shape surrounded by a small negative space appears to be heavier than a small positive shape surrounded by a large negative space

_____ **3.** color

c. a large shape or form appears to be heavier than a small shape or form

_____ **4.** texture

d. a way of organizing parts of a design so that unlike objects have equal visual weight

_____ **5.** position

e. a rough surface has more visual weight than a smooth surface

B. Drawing

Draw a design that illustrates informal balance.

C. Writing

Look at Mary Cassat's *The Tea.* Write a descriptive paragraph that explains how this painting is balanced.

El equilibrio informal

A. Emparejar

Empareja cada palabra de la Columna 1 con su definición en la
Columna 2.

Columna 1

_____ **1.** equilibrio informal

_____ **2.** tamaño

_____ **3.** color

_____ **4.** textura

_____ **5.** posición

Columna 2

a. un color brillante tiene más peso visual que un color opaco

b. un espacio positivo grande rodeado de un espacio negativo
pequeño parece ser más pesado que un espacio
positivo pequeño rodeado de un espacio negativo grande

c. una figura o forma grande parece más pesada que una
figura o forma pequeña

d. una manera de organizar partes de un diseño de modo
que los objetos desiguales tengan el mismo peso visual

e. una superficie áspera tiene más peso visual que una
superficie suave

B. Dibujar

Dibuja un diseño que ilustre el equilibrio informal.

C. Escribir

Mira la obra de Mary Cassat *The Tea.* Escribe un párrafo descriptivo
que explique cómo está equilibrada esta pintura.

_____

_____

_____

Radial Balance

A. Short Answer

Answer the following question.
What is radial balance?

_____

_____

B. Drawing

Create a design that has radial balance in the box below.

C. Writing

Look at *Bull's Eye Quilt* and write a paragraph about the artist's use
of radial balance.

El equilibrio radial

A. Respuesta corta

Contesta la siguiente pregunta.
¿Qué es el equilibrio radial?

_____

_____

B. Dibujar

Crea un diseño eso tiene equilibrio radial en el cuadro siguiente.

C. Escribir

Mira la obra *Bull's Eye Quilt* y escribe un párrafo sobre cómo el artista usó el equilibrio radial.

Emphasis of an Element

A. Fill in the Blank

Complete the following sentence by filling in the blank.

_____ is the principle of design that stresses one
area over another area.

B. Drawing

Draw a nonobjective design. Your design should emphasize line,
color, or shape.

C. Writing

Look at *Great Water Lily of America* and explain how Sharp's use of
emphasis makes you feel.

El énfasis de un elemento

A. Llenar el espacio en blanco

Completa la siguiente oración llenando el espacio en blanco.

_____ es el principio de diseño que destaca un área sobre otra.

B. Dibujar

Dibuja un diseño subjetivo. Tu diseño debe enfatizar una línea, un color o una figura.

C. Escribir

Mira la obra *Great Water Lily of America* y explica cómo el uso del énfasis de Sharp te hace sentir.

Emphasis of an Area

A. Matching

Match each word in Column 1 to its definition in Column 2.

Column 1

_____ **1.** contrast

_____ **2.** focal point

_____ **3.** isolation

_____ **4.** location

Column 2

a. occurs when an object is placed alone and away from the other objects in an artwork

b. occurs when one element stands out from the rest of the work

c. creates emphasis when an object is placed in the center of an artwork

d. the area of emphasis in a work of art

B. Drawing

Use geometric shapes to create one design that uses isolation for emphasis and one design that uses location for emphasis.

isolation   **location**

C. Writing

Study *Conversation Piece* and write a paragraph about the arrangement of the sculptures.

El énfasis de un área

A. Emparejar

Empareja cada palabra de la Columna 1 con su definición en la Columna 2.

Columna 1

_____ **1.** contraste

_____ **2.** punto focal

_____ **3.** aislamiento

_____ **4.** ubicación

Columna 2

a. ocurre cuando un objeto se coloca solo y lejos de los otros objetos de una obra de arte

b. ocurre cuando un elemento resalta entre el resto de la obra

c. crea énfasis cuando un objeto se coloca en el centro de una obra de arte

d. el área de énfasis en una obra de arte

B. Dibujar

Usa figuras geométricas para crear un diseño que use aislamiento para enfatizar y otro diseño que use ubicación para enfatizar.

aislamiento   **ubicación**

C. Escribir

Estudia la obra *Conversation Piece* y escribe un párrafo sobre el arreglo de las esculturas.

_____

_____

_____

_____

Facial Proportions

A. Matching

Match the words in Column 1 with their definitions in Column 2.

Column 1

_____ **1.** central axis

_____ **2.** facial proportions

_____ **3.** profile proportions

_____ **4.** frontal proportions

Column 2

a. a front view of the head that is divided by three horizontal lines across the central axis

b. a real or imaginary dividing line which can run in two directions, vertically and horizontally

c. a side view of the head that is divided by three horizontal lines

d. the relationship of one feature of a face to another feature

B. Drawing

Draw a human face in the box below. Use a central axis line.

C. Writing

Look at Isabel Bishop's *Two Girls* and describe how she used facial proportions.

_____

_____

_____

_____

Las proporciones faciales

A. Emparejar

Empareja las palabras de la Columna 1 con sus definiciones en la
Columna 2.

Columna 1

_____ **1.** eje central

_____ **2.** proporciones faciales

_____ **3.** proporciónes de perfil

_____ **4.** proporciones frontales

Columna 2

a. una vista frontal de la cabeza dividida por tres
líneas horizontales atravesando el eje central

b. una línea divisora real o imaginaria que puede
extenderse en dos direcciones: vertical y horizontal

c. una vista lateral de la cabeza dividida por tres
líneas horizontales

d. la relación de un rasgo de la cara a otro

B. Dibujar

Dibuja un rostro humano en el siguiente cuadro. Uso un eje central.

C. Escribir

Mira la obra *Two Girls* de Isabel Bishop y describe cómo ella usó
las proporciones faciales.

Figure Proportions

A. Fill in the Blanks

Complete the following sentences by writing the missing words in the blanks.

1. _____ the principle of art that is concerned with the size relationship of one part to another.

2. A _____ is a comparison of size between two things.

B. Drawing

Draw a human figure in the box below. Draw a scale showing how many heads tall the person in your drawing is.

C. Writing

Look at *Dancing Lady* and write a paragraph describing how the artist used figure proportions.

Las proporciones de la figura

A. Llenar los espacios en blanco

Completa las siguientes oraciones escribiendo las palabras que faltan en los espacios en blanco.

1. _____ el principio artístico que tiene que ver con la relación de tamaño de una parte a otra.

2. Una _____ es una comparación de tamaño entre dos cosas.

B. Dibujar

Dibuja una figura humana en el siguiente cuadro. Dibuja una escala que muestre cuántas cabezas cabrían en la estatura de la persona en tu dibujo.

C. Escribir

Mira la obra *Dancing Lady* y escribe un párrafo para describir cómo el artista usó las proporciones de la figura.

Facial Distortion

A. Short Answer

Write the answer to the question.

What is distortion? _____

_____

B. Drawing

Draw a human face in the box below. Distort a feature on the face.

C. Writing

Look at the face jugs in this lesson and explain why the artist may
have distorted the facial features.

La distorsión facial

A. ﹝Respuesta corta﹞

Escribe la respuesta a la pregunta.

¿Qué es la distorsión? _____

_____

B. ﹝Dibujar﹞

Dibuja un rostro humano en el siguiente cuadro. Distorsiona un rasgo del rostro.

```



```

C. ﹝Escribir﹞

Mira las jarras con rostros en esta lección y explica por qué el artista pudo haber distorsionado los rasgos faciales.

_____
_____
_____
_____
_____
_____
_____

Figure Distortion

A. Fill in the Blanks

Complete each sentence by writing the missing word in the blank.

1. _____ is an increase or enlargement beyond what is expected or normal.

2. _____ is a deviation from normal or expected proportions.

B. Drawing

Draw a person in the box below. Draw attention to a body feature
on the person by distorting it.

C. Writing

Look at Botero's *Dancing in Colombia* and describe how he used
figure distortion in his artwork.

La distorsión de la figura

A. Llenar los espacios en blanco

Completa cada oración escribiendo la palabra que falta en el
espacio en blanco.

1. _____ es un aumento o agrandamiento más allá de lo normal.

2. _____ es una desviación de lo normal o de las proporciones esperadas.

B. Dibujar

Dibuja a una persona en el siguiente cuadro. Distorsiona un rasgo
del cuerpo de la persona para llamar la atención a esa parte.

C. Escribir

Mira la obra *Dancing in Colombia* de Botero y describe cómo él usó
la distorsión de la figura en su obra de arte.

Realistic Scale

A. Fill in the Blanks

Complete each sentence by writing the missing word in the blank.

1. _____ is when an artist creates a work of art where everything fits together and makes sense in size relation.

2. _____ refers to size as measured against a standard reference.

B. Drawing

Draw an object using a realistic scale.

C. Writing

Look at *Leonardo da Vinci Chair* by Julia Russell and explain why this is an example of realistic scale.

La escala realista

A. Llenar los espacios en blanco

Completa cada oración escribiendo la palabra que falta en el
espacio en blanco.

1. _____ es cuando un artista crea una obra de arte en la cual todo corresponde y
tiene sentido en cuanto a la relación de tamaño.

2. _____ se refiere al tamaño al medirse contra una referencia normal.

B. Dibujar

Dibuja un objeto usando una escala realista.

C. Escribir

Mira la obra *Leonardo da Vinci Chair* de Julia Russell y explica por
qué ésta es un ejemplo de una escala realista.

Unrealistic Scale

A. Matching

Match the words in Column 1 with their definitions in Column 2.

Column 1

_____ **1.** unrealistic scale

_____ **2.** ratio

_____ **3.** realistic scale

Column 2

a. size as measured against a standard reference

b. when an artist creates a work of art where everything fits together and makes sense in size relation

c. when an artist makes size relationships that do not make sense

B. Drawing

Draw an outdoor scene in the box below using unrealistic scale.

C. Writing

Look at Salvador Dalí's *Persistence of Memory* and explain why it is an example of unrealistic scale.

La escala irreal

A. Emparejar

Empareja las palabras de la Columna 1 con sus definiciones en la Columna 2.

Columna 1

_____ **1.** escala irreal

_____ **2.** razón

_____ **3.** escala realista

Columna 2

a. el tamaño al medirse contra una referencia normal

b. cuando un artista crea una obra de arte en la cual todo corresponde y tiene sentido en cuanto a la relación del tamaño

c. cuando un artista crea relaciones de tamaño que no tienen sentido

B. Dibujar

Dibuja una escena al aire libre en el siguiente cuadro usando una escala irreal.

C. Escribir

Mira la obra *Persistence of Memory* de Salvador Dalí y explica por qué ésta es un ejemplo de una escala irreal.

Variety Through Line, Shape, and Color

A. Short Answer

Complete the sentence.

Variety is the principle of art that _____

_____ .

B. Drawing

Draw a picture of your school. Use variety in your picture.

C. Writing

Study Lee Bennion's *Snow Queen, Portrait of Adah,* and write a paragraph describing the variety in this artwork.

La variedad a través de la línea, la figura y el color

A. Respuesta corta

Completa la oración.

La variedad es el principio artístico que _____

_____.

B. Dibujar

Dibuja una pintura de tu escuela. Usa variedad en tu pintura.

C. Escribir

Estudia la obra *Snow Queen, Portrait of Adah* de Lee Bennion y
escribe un párrafo para describir la variedad en esta obra de arte.

Variety Through Contrast

A. Short Answer

Complete this sentence.

An artist often uses contrast to _____

_____ .

B. Drawing

Draw a picture of an animal and show variety through contrast.

C. Writing

Study Paul Brach's *Chuska* and write a paragraph describing the contrast in this artwork.

La variedad a través del contraste

A. Respuesta corta

Completa esta oración.

A menudo, un artista usa contraste para _____

_____ .

B. Dibujar

Haz un dibujo de un animal y muestra variedad a través del contraste.

C. Escribir

Estudia la obra *Chuska* de Paul Brach y escribe un párrafo para describir el contraste en esta obra de arte.

_____

_____

_____

_____

_____

_____

Harmony in Two-Dimensional Art

A. Fill in the Blank

Complete the following sentence by filling in the blank.

_____ is the principle of art which creates unity by stressing similarities

of separate but related parts.

B. Drawing

Create harmony using either color, shape, or line in the box below.
Indicate which element you have used by writing *color, shape,* or *line*
on the line provided.

_____

C. Writing

Study *Woman's Headcloth* and write a descriptive paragraph about
the elements that are repeated to create harmony in the artwork.

La armonía en el arte bidimensional

A. Llenar los espacios en blanco

Completa la siguiente oración llenando el espacio en blanco.

_____ es el principio artístico que crea unidad al destacar las semejanzas de las partes separadas pero relacionadas.

B. Dibujar

Crea armonía usando el color, la figura o la línea en el siguiente cuadro. Escribe *color, figura* o *línea* en la línea dada para indicar qué elemento usaste.

_____

C. Escribir

Estudia la obra *Woman's Headcloth* y escribe un párrafo descriptivo acerca de los elementos que se repiten para crear armonía en la obra de arte.

_____

_____

_____

_____

_____

Harmony in Three-Dimensional Art

A. Short Answer

Complete each sentence.

1. Harmony is _____

_____ .

2. An assemblage is _____

_____ .

B. Drawing

Draw a design for an assemblage.

C. Writing

Study *White Vertical Water* by Louise Nevelson and explain how she created harmony in the artwork.

La armonía en el arte tridimensional

A. Respuesta corta

Completa cada oración.

1. La armonía es _____

_____ .

2. Un collage es _____

_____ .

B. Dibujar

Dibuja un diseño para un collage.

C. Escribir

Estudia la obra *White Vertical Water* de Louise Nevelson y explica cómo ella creó armonía en la obra de arte.

Unity in Weaving

A. **Short Answer**

Answer the following questions.

1. What is unity? _____

2. How is unity created in a work of art? _____

_____

B. **Drawing**

Draw a design for a weaving.

C. **Writing**

Look at the works of art from this lesson and explain why weaving
is an example of unity.

La unidad en el tejido

A. Respuesta corta

Contesta las siguientes preguntas.

1. ¿Qué es la unidad? _____

2. ¿Cómo se crea unidad en una obra de arte? _____

_____

B. Dibujar

Dibuja un diseño para un tejido.

C. Escribir

Mira las obras de arte en esta lección y explica por qué el tejido es
un ejemplo de unidad.

Unity in Three-Dimensional Art

A. Fill in the Blanks

Complete the sentence below by filling in the blanks.

Artists create _____ when they balance the art

principles of _____ and _____.

B. Drawing

Draw a design for a sculpture that shows unity.

C. Writing

Look at Nam June Paik's *Eagle Eye* and write a paragraph that explains how he created unity in this sculpture.

La unidad en el arte tridimensional

A. Llenar los espacios en blanco

Completa la siguiente oración llenando los espacios en blanco.

Los artistas crean _____ cuando equilibran los principios

artísticos de _____ y _____ .

B. Dibujar

Dibuja un diseño para una escultura que muestre unidad.

C. Escribir

Mira la obra *Eagle Eye* de Nam June Paik y escribe un párrafo que
explique cómo él creó unidad en esta escultura.

Answer Key

Unit 1

Lesson 1

A. 1. e
    2. b
    3. d
    4. a
    5. c

B. Students will draw a different line in each of the boxes. Make sure each line is labeled correctly.

C. In *Ceremonial Skirt* the lines are more linear, or straight. In *Plate 24* they are mostly curved lines.

Lesson 2

A. 1. b
    2. c
    3. a
    4. d

B. Students will draw a different shape in each of the five boxes. Make sure each shape is labeled correctly.

C. In *Pictorial Quilt* free-form shapes, such as human figures, animals, and shooting stars are repeated.

Lesson 3

A. 1. a three-dimensional object that is measured by height, width, and depth
    2. like geometric shapes, are based on mathematical formulas with precise measurements

B. Students will draw and label three geometric forms. Make sure each geometric form is labeled correctly.

C. In *Cubi XVII*, the forms are made of rectangles, circles, and squares. The forms that look like rectangles and squares have six surfaces: top, bottom, both sides, front, and back. The cylinder form has three surfaces: the top and bottom and the continuous curved tube.

Lesson 4

A. 1. a three-dimensional objects with an uneven or irregular edge
    2. natural or organic form

B. Students will label and draw three free-form forms. Make sure each free-form form is labeled correctly.

C. In *Fish Story* there are the following forms: a fish, driftwood, a man, a boy, and a fishing pole. Each form has details, especially the man and the boy whose facial expressions can be seen.

Lesson 5

A. 1. b
    2. c
    3. a
    4. d

B. Drawings will vary but should include three perspective techniques.

C. Both artists used overlapping to create depth on a two-dimensional surface. People are overlapping in van Gogh's and Pannini's paintings. Also parts of buildings are overlapping in van Gogh's painting.

Answer Key

Lesson 6

A.
1. the areas above, below, between, within, and around an object
2. the shapes and forms
3. the area or empty spaces between the shapes or forms

B. Drawings will vary.

C. There is little negative space in *Seated Man #4,* which gives it a heavy feeling. There is a lot of negative space in *Proposal for a Monument to Apollinaire,* giving it a light, airy feeling.

Unit 2 Lesson 1

A.
1. e
2. b
3. a
4. c
5. d

B.
1. primary
2. secondary
3. secondary
4. primary

C. In both works of art the primary colors are red, yellow, and blue; the secondary colors are orange, green, and violet. *Anna and David* also has the intermediate colors yellow-green and yellow-orange. *Conception Synchromy* has the intermediate colors blue-violet and red-violet. Both works of art have the neutral colors black and white.

Lesson 2

A.
1. a
2. d
3. b
4. e
5. c
6. f

B. Students will label and draw three shading techniques. Shading techniques should be labeled correctly.

C. The left side of the painting has more lighted areas than the right side, including the snow-covered roof, the area of snow between the distant house and the fence, and the snow in the foreground. There are dark values/shades in the area between the first tree in the front and the stand of trees in the middle and background, including the shadows cast by the trees and house in the background. A gradual change in value occurs on the right side of the middle ground, moving from a middle value back toward a darker value.

Lesson 3

A.
1. the brightness or dullness of a color
2. colors that are opposite each other on the color wheel

B.
1. green
2. orange
3. violet

C. Answers will vary. Students may say that Derain used these colors to create a quiet or sad mood.

Answer Key

Lesson 4

A.
1. c
2. d
3. a
4. b

B. Students will paint two sets of analogous colors in the boxes. Analogous sets should be labeled correctly.

C. Yellow catches the viewer's attention first in *Fireworks.* When placed next to the blue, the yellow and then the orange come forward, causing the blue to recede. The yellow also takes up the largest area in the painting and is in the center. In *Fishing Boats,* white is noticed first because it is the brightest color in the painting.

Lesson 5

A.
1. c
2. a
3. b

B.
1. Answers will vary. Examples might include: gravel
2. Answers will vary. Examples might include: a glass bottle
3. Answers will vary. Examples might include: polished silver
4. Answers will vary. Examples might include: sandpaper

C. The character's shirt appears rough, like burlap. The visual textures in the foreground and the background might also appear rough to students because they look like sandpaper.

Lesson 6

A.
1. a texture you can touch and feel
2. an art object that is created from an assortment of media

B. Drawings will vary.

C. *Coming of Age Hat:* The raised areas on the top of the hat, the red and green areas, and the beads hanging on either side of the hat are rough. The dark blue area of the brim and the golden forms on either side of the hat are smooth. The dark vertical rows of material are matte. The golden fabric and tassels are shiny. *Kings Crown:* The beaded strands hanging from the brim are rough. The strips around the brim are smooth. The small dark-blue area at the base of the crown is matte. The beadwork is shiny.

Unit 3 Lesson 1

A.
1. a unit that is made of objects or art elements that are repeated
2. a repeated surface decoration

B. Students will draw a motif and a pattern. The motif and pattern should be labeled correctly.

C. The colors blue and white could represent the ocean and breaking waves. The repeated white free-form shapes look like waves.

Lesson 2

A.
1. d
2. c
3. a
4. e
5. b

Answer Key

B. Students will draw random, regular, and alternating patterns. Patterns should be labeled correctly.

C. *King:* Colors: Warm and cool colors, complementary set of green and red. Lines: Repeated curves throughout the work, the only straight lines are on either side of the nose. Shapes: Free-form or organic shapes are the face and flowers; geometric shapes used are circles in the crown and eyes and ovals. *Indian Fantasy:* Colors: red, yellow, green and the neutral colors of black and white, complementary set of green and red. Lines: Repeated curves and straight lines throughout the work, zigzag lines are created by the repeated teepees in the lower portion of the painting and the yellow feathers of the birds wings. Shapes: Free-form or organic shapes in the fish, tepee, and canoe designs and fire images, geometric shapes used are circles, triangles, and rectangles throughout painting.

Lesson 3

A. 1. regular, random, and alternating
   2. drawing and painting or by adding like objects to the surface

B. The students will draw two patterns. Patterns should be labeled correctly.

C. Answers will vary. Students may say that the colors used in the patterns on *Carved Animals* make them interesting. Students also may say that the details of the patterns on *Ceramic Figures* make them interesting.

Lesson 4

A. 1. the principle of design that organizes the elements of art in a work by repeating elements and/or objects
   2. repeated positive shapes separated by negative spaces

B. Drawings will vary.

C. Picasso used both curved and straight lines that are repeated. The horizontal and vertical lines run parallel to one another in the background. There are repeated curved lines in the hair and neck. There are straight intersecting lines in the clothing.

Lesson 5

A. 1. the principle of art that leads a viewer's eyes through a work of art
   2. repeating the art elements or objects

B. 1. yes
   2. yes
   3. no
   4. yes

C. No. *Bottom of the Ravine* is calm because it is a landscape of a mountainous area. There is not any particular action happening, whereas *Exotic Landscape* has animals swinging from one side of the painting to the other.

Lesson 6

A. 1. c
   2. a
   3. b

B. 1. yes
   2. no
   3. yes
   4. no

Answer Key

C. Answers will vary. Rose's mobile is more abstract; therefore, it does not seem like he is trying to capture the movement of a real image.

Unit 4 Lesson 1

A.
1. b
2. d
3. a
4. c

B. Designs will vary but should include a central axis.

C. The shapes are arranged as a long set of five rectangles. The central rectangular building form has a set of horizontal steps leading up to the front of the structure. There are two squares in front of two rectangular shapes, and a line of eight columns supports a rectangle on which a triangular shape sits. On either side are four more columns with another large rectangular form on either side of these.

Lesson 2

A.
1. Approximate symmetry is a type of balance that is almost symmetrical but small differences in the artwork make it more interesting.
2. To avoid boring the viewer, artists will often use approximate symmetry.

B. Still lifes will vary.

C. The figure of Vibert is placed in the center of the picture plane, taking up almost half of the canvas. He appears symmetrical at first, but tiny details keep the image from being perfectly symmetrical. The part on the viewer's left side, the thickness of his hair on the right, the pocket on the right side of the jacket, and the added wrinkles on the left sleeve contribute to this not being perfectly symmetrical.

Lesson 3

A.
1. d
2. c
3. a
4. e
5. b

B. Designs will vary.

C. The two women are sitting on the left side of the painting on a red and white couch. In front of the figures and to the right of the painting is the top of a red table on which a silver tea set sits. To the far right is half of a mantle supported by a white fireplace, and above it is a portion of a painting.

Lesson 4

A. Radial balance is a type of balance that occurs when the art elements come out, or radiate, from a central point.

B. Designs will vary.

Answer Key

C. Student responses will vary based on how they interpret the quilt. Some may say that the quilt starts in the center and that the other fabrics were added to it in an outward pattern. Others may say that each section was made separately, and then layered on top of one another.

Lesson 5
A. Emphasis
B. Designs will vary.
C. Answers will vary based on students' experiences. Some may say the emphasis makes them feel happy because it reminds them of spring when flowers begin to bloom.

Lesson 6
A. 1. b
    2. d
    3. a
    4. c
B. Designs will vary.
C. There are three figures together whose heads are tilted toward one another. One arm reaches around to touch the back of another one of the figures. Two figures are placed away from the group—one to the far right, the other to the far left, both are reaching toward the group of three.

Unit 5 Lesson 1
A. 1. b
    2. d
    3. c
    4. a

B. Faces will vary but students should draw a central axis line.
C. Frontal view of the woman: The top of the ear lines up with the top of the eye, and the bottom of the ear lines up with the bottom of the nose. Profile of the woman: The top of the ear lines up with the top of the brow, and the bottom of the ear lines up with the bottom of the nose.

Lesson 2
A. 1. Figure proportions
    2. ratio
B. Figures will vary but students should include a scale showing how many heads tall the person is.
C. *Dancing Lady* looks life-sized, but it is not. This is because the figure has been carved in perfect proportion, which is written as the ratio 1:6.

Lesson 3
A. Distortion is a deviation from normal or expected proportions.
B. Faces will vary but one feature should be distorted.
C. Answers will vary. Students might say that the artist distorted the facial features to catch the viewer's attention or express different emotions.

Answer Key

Lesson 4
A. 1. Exaggeration
   2. Distortion
B. Drawings will vary but one feature should be distorted.
C. Fernando Botero rounded all of the people in *Dancing in Colombia*. The figures look as if they are blown up or inflated. The size of the features is small in comparison to the size of the face.

Lesson 5
A. 1. Realistic scale
   2. Scale
B. Designs will vary.
C. Student responses will vary based on personal experiences. However, many students will say that they believe the chair is an example of realistic scale because they may have seen or sat in a chair similar to this before.

Lesson 6
A. 1. c
   2. a
   3. b
B. Designs will vary.
C. Student responses will vary based on personal experiences. However, many students will say that many of the objects in the painting are larger than they would be in real life.

Unit 6 Lesson 1
A. is concerned with difference or contrast
B. Drawings will vary.

C. The painting shows contrasts of shape and size. There is a contrast of warm and cool colors, as well as some contrast of patterns. Bennion used mixed free-form and geometric shapes to create variety.

Lesson 2
A. keep our attention on a certain part of an artwork
B. Drawings will vary.
C. The dark-red horses are emerging from the lighter-red ground, and the dark mountain is emerging from the lighter-red ground. The value of the sky is the same as the value of the ground, which creates a feeling of mystery.

Lesson 3
A. Harmony
B. Designs will vary.
C. There are horizontal, vertical, and diagonal lines in various objects. There is an abundance of triangular shapes used to create the figures. The people and animals are free-from shapes. There are mostly warm colors in the embroidery.

Lesson 4
A. 1. the principle of art that creates unity by stressing similarities of separate but related parts
   2. a variety of objects assembled to create one complete piece
B. Designs will vary.

Answer Key

C. Nevelson created harmony by using one color (white) and similar rectangular boxes that hold the wooden forms.

Lesson 5

A. 1. Unity is the feeling of wholeness or oneness that is achieved by properly using the elements and principles in art.

2. Unity is created when the art principles of variety and harmony work together.

B. Designs will vary.

C. In weaving, the separate parts relate to make a whole weaving. Even though the piece may be made of various lines, shapes, and colors, these elements are woven together. One way that variety and harmony work together to create unity or oneness is by the very technique of weaving.

Lesson 6

A. unity, variety, harmony

B. Designs will vary.

C. Paik combined old technology—the old slide projector and eye chart—with new technology—computers—to create a unified figure based on the Native American thunderbird.

Name _____ Date _____ Lesson _____

Creative Expression Rubrics

Level 6 • Unit I • Lesson I

	Art History and Culture	Aesthetic Perception	Creative Expression	Art Criticism
3 POINTS	The student demonstrates knowledge of Henri Matisse and Indonesian art.	The student accurately defines line types and qualities in a work of art.	The student's contour drawing demonstrates how to use line and line qualities.	The student thoughtfully and honestly evaluates his or her own work using the four steps of art criticism.
2 POINTS	The student's knowledge of Henri Matisse and Indonesian art is weak or incomplete.	The student shows emerging awareness of line types and qualities but cannot consistently identify them.	The student's contour drawing shows some awareness of how to use line and line qualities.	The student attempts to evaluate his or her own work but shows an incomplete understanding of evaluation criteria.
1 POINT	The student cannot demonstrate knowledge of Henri Matisse and Indonesian art.	The student cannot identify line types and qualities.	The student's contour drawing shows no understanding of how to use line and line qualities.	The student makes no attempt to evaluate his or her own work.

Level 6 • Unit I • Lesson 2

	Art History and Culture	Aesthetic Perception	Creative Expression	Art Criticism
3 POINTS	The student demonstrates knowledge of North American quiltmaking.	The student accurately identifies geometric and free-form shapes in a work of art.	The student's quilt square clearly demonstrates the use of geometric and free-form shapes.	The student thoughtfully and honestly evaluates his or her own work using the four steps of art criticism.
2 POINTS	The student's knowledge of North American quiltmaking is weak or incomplete.	The student shows emerging awareness of geometric and free-form shapes but cannot consistently identify them.	The student's quilt square shows some awareness of geometric or free-form shapes.	The student attempts to evaluate his or her own work but shows an incomplete understanding of evaluation criteria.
1 POINT	The student cannot demonstrate knowledge of North American quiltmaking.	The student cannot define or identify geometric and free-form shapes.	The student's quilt square shows no understanding of geometric or free-form shapes.	The student makes no attempt to evaluate his or her own work.

Creative Expression Rubrics

Level 6 • Unit I • Lesson 3

Art History and Culture	Aesthetic Perception	Creative Expression	Art Criticism
3 POINTS The student demonstrates knowledge of the lives and work of David Smith and George Hart.	The student accurately identifies geometric forms in a work of art.	The student's freestanding sculpture clearly demonstrates using geometric forms.	The student thoughtfully and honestly evaluates his or her own work using the four steps of art criticism.
2 POINTS The student's knowledge of David Smith and George Hart is weak or incomplete.	The student shows emerging awareness of geometric forms but cannot consistently identify them.	The student's freestanding sculpture shows some awareness of geometric forms.	The student attempts to evaluate his or her own work but shows an incomplete understanding of evaluation criteria.
1 POINT The student cannot demonstrate knowledge of David Smith or George Hart.	The student cannot identify geometric forms.	The student's freestanding sculpture shows no understanding of geometric forms.	The student makes no attempt to evaluate his or her own work.

Level 6 • Unit I • Lesson 4

Art History and Culture	Aesthetic Perception	Creative Expression	Art Criticism
3 POINTS The student demonstrates knowledge of the lives and work of Paul Baliker and John Warren.	The student accurately identifies free-form forms in the three-dimensional sculpture.	The student's sculpture model clearly demonstrates using free-form forms.	The student thoughtfully and honestly evaluates his or her own work using the four steps of art criticism.
2 POINTS The student's knowledge of the lives and work of Paul Baliker and John Warren is weak or incomplete.	The student shows emerging awareness of free-form forms in three-dimensional sculpture but cannot consistently identify them.	The student's sculpture model shows some awareness of free-form forms.	The student attempts to evaluate his or her own work but shows an incomplete understanding of evaluation criteria.
1 POINT The student cannot demonstrate knowledge of the lives and work of Paul Baliker and John Warren.	The student cannot identify free-form forms.	The student's sculpture model shows no understanding of free-form forms.	The student makes no attempt to evaluate his or her own work.

Name _____ Date _____ Lesson _____

Creative Expression Rubrics

Level 6 • Unit 1 • Lesson 5

	Art History and Culture	Aesthetic Perception	Creative Expression	Art Criticism
3 POINTS	The student demonstrates knowledge of the lives and work of Giovanni Pannini and Vincent van Gogh.	The student accurately identifies the use of space in two-dimensional works of art.	The student's one-point linear perspective drawing clearly demonstrates using perspective techniques to create space.	The student thoughtfully and honestly evaluates his or her own work using the four steps of art criticism.
2 POINTS	The student's knowledge of the lives and work of Giovanni Pannini and Vincent van Gogh is weak or incomplete.	The student shows emerging awareness of the use of space in two-dimensional works of art but cannot consistently identify it.	The student's one-point linear perspective drawing shows some awareness of perspective techniques to create space and depth.	The student attempts to evaluate his or her own work but shows an incomplete understanding of evaluation criteria.
1 POINT	The student cannot demonstrate knowledge of the lives and work of Giovanni Pannini and Vincent van Gogh.	The student cannot identify how space is used.	The student's one-point linear perspective drawing shows no understanding of how to create space and depth.	The student makes no attempt to evaluate his or her own work.

Level 6 • Unit 1 • Lesson 6

	Art History and Culture	Aesthetic Perception	Creative Expression	Art Criticism
3 POINTS	The student demonstrates knowledge of the lives and work of Pablo Picasso and David Bates.	The student accurately identifies the use of positive and negative space in two-dimensional works of art.	The student's assemblage clearly demonstrates the use of positive and negative space.	The student thoughtfully and honestly evaluates his or her own work using the four steps of art criticism.
2 POINTS	The student's knowledge of the lives and work of Pablo Picasso and David Bates is weak or incomplete.	The student shows emerging awareness of the use of positive and negative space in two-dimensional works of art but cannot consistently identify it.	The student's assemblage shows some awareness of positive and negative space.	The student attempts to evaluate his or her own work but shows an incomplete understanding of evaluation criteria.
1 POINT	The student cannot demonstrate knowledge of the lives and work of Pablo Picasso and David Bates.	The student cannot identify how positive and negative space is used.	The student's assemblage shows no understanding of positive and negative space.	The student makes no attempt to evaluate his or her own work.

Creative Expression Rubrics

Level 6 • Unit 2 • Lesson 1

	Art History and Culture	Aesthetic Perception	Creative Expression	Art Criticism
3 POINTS	The student demonstrates knowledge of the lives and work of Miriam Schapiro and Stanton MacDonald-Wright.	The student accurately identifies the use of spectral color in two- and three-dimensional works of art.	The student's color wheel clearly demonstrates how to mix and organize the color spectrum.	The student thoughtfully and honestly evaluates his or her own work using the four steps of art criticism.
2 POINTS	The student's knowledge of the lives and work of Miriam Schapiro and Stanton MacDonald-Wright is weak or incomplete.	The student shows an emerging awareness of spectral colors in two- and three-dimensional art but cannot consistently identify them.	The student's color wheel shows some awareness of how to mix and organize the color spectrum.	The student attempts to evaluate his or her own work but shows an incomplete understanding of evaluation criteria.
1 POINT	The student cannot demonstrate knowledge of the lives and work of Miriam Schapiro or Stanton MacDonald-Wright.	The student cannot identify how spectral colors are used.	The student's color wheel shows no understanding of how to mix or organize the color spectrum.	The student makes no attempt to evaluate his or her own work.

Level 6 • Unit 2 • Lesson 2

	Art History and Culture	Aesthetic Perception	Creative Expression	Art Criticism
3 POINTS	The student demonstrates knowledge of the lives and work of Vincent van Gogh and John Henry Twachtman.	The student accurately identifies the use of value in drawings and paintings.	The student's monochromatic landscape clearly demonstrates use of value, tints, and shades.	The student thoughtfully and honestly evaluates his or her own work using the four steps of art criticism.
2 POINTS	The student's knowledge of Vincent van Gogh and John Henry Twachtman is weak or incomplete.	The student shows an emerging awareness of value in drawings and paintings but cannot identify it consistently.	The student's monochromatic landscape shows some use of value, tints, and shades.	The student attempts to evaluate his or her own work but shows an incomplete understanding of evaluation criteria.
1 POINT	The student cannot demonstrate knowledge of Vincent van Gogh or John Henry Twachtman.	The student cannot identify uses of value.	The student's monochromatic landscape shows no understanding of value, tints, or shades.	The student makes no attempt to evaluate his or her own work.

Creative Expression Rubrics

Level 6 • Unit 2 • Lesson 3

	Art History and Culture	Aesthetic Perception	Creative Expression	Art Criticism
3 POINTS	The student can demonstrate knowledge of the lives and work of Andre Derain and Karl Schmidt-Rottluff.	The student accurately identifies use of color intensity in two-dimensional art.	The student's portrait demonstrates uses of color intensity.	The student thoughtfully and honestly evaluates his or her own work using the four steps of art criticism.
2 POINTS	The student's knowledge of Andre Derain and Karl Schmidt-Rottluff is weak or incomplete.	The student shows an emerging awareness of color intensity in two-dimensional art but cannot identify it consistently.	The student's portrait shows some use of color intensity.	The student attempts to evaluate his or her own work but shows an incomplete understanding of evaluation criteria.
1 POINT	The student cannot demonstrate knowledge of Andre Derain or Karl Schmidt-Rottluff.	The student cannot identify uses of color intensity.	The student's portrait shows no understanding of color intensity.	The student makes no attempt to evaluate his or her own work.

Level 6 • Unit 2 • Lesson 4

	Art History and Culture	Aesthetic Perception	Creative Expression	Art Criticism
3 POINTS	The student demonstrates knowledge of the lives and work of James Ensor and Georges Braque.	The student accurately identifies use of color schemes in two-dimensional art.	The student's landscape series demonstrates a good understanding of how to use different color schemes.	The student thoughtfully and honestly evaluates his or her own work using the four steps of art criticism.
2 POINTS	The student's knowledge of the lives and work of James Ensor and Georges Braque is weak or incomplete.	The student shows an emerging awareness of color schemes in two-dimensional art but cannot identify it consistently.	The student's landscape series shows some use and understanding of different color schemes.	The student attempts to evaluate his or her own work but shows an incomplete understanding of evaluation criteria.
1 POINT	The student cannot demonstrate knowledge of the lives and work of James Ensor or Georges Braque.	The student cannot identify use of color schemes.	The student's landscape series shows no understanding of color schemes.	The student makes no attempt to evaluate his or her own work.

Creative Expression Rubrics

Level 6 • Unit 2 • Lesson 5

	Art History and Culture	Aesthetic Perception	Creative Expression	Art Criticism
3 POINTS	The student demonstrates knowledge of the lives and work of Jean-Baptiste Simeon Chardin and Susan LeVan.	The student accurately identifies the use of texture in two-dimensional works of art.	The student's computer drawing clearly demonstrates the use of visual texture.	The student thoughtfully and honestly evaluates his or her own work using the four steps of art criticism.
2 POINTS	The student's knowledge of Jean-Baptiste Simeon Chardin and Susan LeVan is weak or incomplete.	The student shows an emerging awareness of texture in two-dimensional artwork but cannot consistently identify them.	The student's computer drawing shows some awareness of visual texture.	The student attempts to evaluate his or her own work but shows an incomplete understanding of evaluation criteria.
1 POINT	The student cannot demonstrate knowledge of the lives and work of Jean-Baptiste Simeon Chardin or Susan LeVan.	The student cannot identify how texture is used.	The student's computer drawing shows no understanding of how to create visual texture.	The student makes no attempt to evaluate his or her own work.

Level 6 • Unit 2 • Lesson 6

	Art History and Culture	Aesthetic Perception	Creative Expression	Art Criticism
3 POINTS	The student demonstrates knowledge of African and Chinese headpieces.	The student accurately identifies the use of tactile textures in three-dimensional forms.	The student's celebratory hat clearly demonstrates use of tactile texture.	The student thoughtfully and honestly evaluates his or her own work using the four steps of art criticism.
2 POINTS	The student's knowledge of African and Chinese headpieces is weak or incomplete.	The student shows an emerging awareness of tactile textures in three-dimensional forms but cannot consistently identify them.	The student's celebratory hat shows some awareness of tactile texture.	The student attempts to evaluate his or her own work but shows an incomplete understanding of evaluation criteria.
1 POINT	The student cannot demonstrate knowledge of African or Chinese headpieces.	The student cannot identify how tactile texture is used in three-dimensional forms.	The student's celebratory hat shows no understanding of how to create tactile texture.	The student makes no attempt to evaluate his or her own work.

Creative Expression Rubrics

Level 6 • Unit 3 • Lesson 1

	Art History and Culture	Aesthetic Perception	Creative Expression	Art Criticism
3 POINTS	The student demonstrates knowledge of the Kwakwaka'wakw and the Egungun.	The student accurately identifies the use of motif and pattern in two- and three-dimensional works of art.	The student's costume design clearly demonstrates how to use motif and pattern.	The student thoughtfully and honestly evaluates his or her own work using the four steps of art criticism.
2 POINTS	The student's knowledge of the Kwakwaka'wakw and the Egungun is weak or incomplete.	The student shows an emerging awareness of motif and pattern in two- and three-dimensional art but cannot consistently identify them.	The student's costume design shows some awareness of how to use motif and pattern.	The student attempts to evaluate his or her own work but shows an incomplete understanding of evaluation criteria.
1 POINT	The student cannot demonstrate knowledge of the Kwakwaka'wakw and the Egungun.	The student cannot identify how motif and pattern are used.	The student's costume design shows no understanding of how to use motif and pattern.	The student makes no attempt to evaluate his or her own work.

Level 6 • Unit 3 • Lesson 2

	Art History and Culture	Aesthetic Perception	Creative Expression	Art Criticism
3 POINTS	The student demonstrates knowledge of the lives and work of Marsden Hartley and Minnie Evans.	The student accurately identifies the use of different pattern types in two-dimensional works of art.	The student's nonobjective design clearly demonstrates how to use different pattern types.	The student thoughtfully and honestly evaluates his or her own work using the four steps of art criticism.
2 POINTS	The student's knowledge of Marsden Hartley and Minnie Evans is weak or incomplete.	The student shows an emerging awareness of different pattern types in two-dimensional art but cannot consistently identify them.	The student's nonobjective design shows some awareness of how to use different pattern types.	The student attempts to evaluate his or her own work but shows an incomplete understanding of evaluation criteria.
1 POINT	The student cannot demonstrate knowledge of Marsden Hartley or Minnie Evans.	The student cannot identify how different pattern types are used.	The student's nonobjective design shows no understanding of how to use different pattern types.	The student makes no attempt to evaluate his or her own work.

Creative Expression Rubrics

Level 6 • Unit 3 • Lesson 3

	Art History and Culture	Aesthetic Perception	Creative Expression	Art Criticism
3 POINTS	The student demonstrates knowledge of the lives and work of Teodora Blanco and Oaxacan sculptors.	The student accurately identifies use of patterns on three-dimensional works of art.	The student's clay animal demonstrates using pattern.	The student thoughtfully and honestly evaluates his or her own work using the four steps of art criticism.
2 POINTS	The student's knowledge of Teodora Blanco and Oaxacan sculptors is weak or incomplete.	The student shows an emerging awareness of patterns on three-dimensional works of art but cannot identify it consistently.	The student's clay animal shows some use of pattern.	The student attempts to evaluate his or her own work but shows an incomplete understanding of evaluation criteria.
1 POINT	The student cannot demonstrate knowledge of Teodora Blanco or Oaxacan sculptors.	The student cannot identify use of patterns on three-dimensional works of art.	The student's clay animal shows no understanding of pattern.	The student makes no attempt to evaluate his or her own work.

Level 6 • Unit 3 • Lesson 4

	Art History and Culture	Aesthetic Perception	Creative Expression	Art Criticism
3 POINTS	The student demonstrates knowledge of the lives and work of Franz Marc and Pablo Picasso.	The student accurately identifies use of visual rhythm in two-dimensional art.	The student's nonobjective design demonstrates a good understanding of how to use visual rhythm.	The student thoughtfully and honestly evaluates his or her own work using the four steps of art criticism.
2 POINTS	The student's knowledge of Franz Marc and Pablo Picasso is weak or incomplete.	The student shows an emerging awareness of visual rhythm in two-dimensional art but cannot identify it consistently.	The student's nonobjective design shows some use and understanding of visual rhythm.	The student attempts to evaluate his or her own work but shows an incomplete understanding of evaluation criteria.
1 POINT	The student cannot demonstrate knowledge of Franz Marc and Pablo Picasso.	The student cannot identify use of visual rhythm.	The student's nonobjective design shows no understanding of visual rhythm.	The student makes no attempt to evaluate his or her own work.

Creative Expression Rubrics

Level 6 • Unit 3 • Lesson 5

	Art History and Culture	Aesthetic Perception	Creative Expression	Art Criticism
3 POINTS	The student demonstrates knowledge of the lives and work of Henri Rousseau and Paul Cézanne.	The student accurately identifies the use of visual movement in two-dimensional works of art.	The student's fantasy landscape clearly demonstrates using visual movement.	The student thoughtfully and honestly evaluates his or her own work using the four steps of art criticism.
2 POINTS	The student's knowledge of Henri Rousseau and Paul Cézanne is weak or incomplete.	The student shows an emerging awareness of visual movement in two-dimensional works of art but cannot consistently identify them.	The student's fantasy landscape shows some awareness of visual movement.	The student attempts to evaluate his or her own work but shows an incomplete understanding of evaluation criteria.
1 POINT	The student cannot demonstrate knowledge of Henri Rousseau and Paul Cézanne.	The student cannot identify how visual movement is used.	The student's fantasy landscape shows no understanding of how to create visual movement.	The student makes no attempt to evaluate his or her own work.

Level 6 • Unit 3 • Lesson 6

	Art History and Culture	Aesthetic Perception	Creative Expression	Art Criticism
3 POINTS	The student demonstrates knowledge of the lives and work of Alexander Calder and Tim Rose.	The student accurately identifies the use of kinetic movement in three-dimensional objects.	The student's mobile demonstrates using kinetic movement.	The student thoughtfully and honestly evaluates his or her own work using the four steps of art criticism.
2 POINTS	The student's knowledge of Alexander Calder and Tim Rose is weak or incomplete.	The student shows an emerging awareness of kinetic movement in three-dimensional objects but cannot consistently identify them.	The student's mobile shows some awareness of kinetic movement.	The student attempts to evaluate his or her own work but shows an incomplete understanding of evaluation criteria.
1 POINT	The student cannot demonstrate knowledge of Alexander Calder and Tim Rose.	The student cannot identify how kinetic movement is used.	The student's mobile shows no understanding of how to use kinetic movement.	The student makes no attempt to evaluate his or her own work.

Creative Expression Rubrics

Level 6 • Unit 4 • Lesson 1

	Art History and Culture	Aesthetic Perception	Creative Expression	Art Criticism
3 POINTS	The student demonstrates knowledge of the United States Capitol and Eiffel Tower.	The student accurately identifies the use of formal or symmetrical balance in architectural structures.	The student's public building design demonstrates how to use formal or symmetrical balance.	The student thoughtfully and honestly evaluates his or her own work using the four steps of art criticism.
2 POINTS	The student's knowledge of the United States Capitol and Eiffel Tower is weak or incomplete.	The student shows an emerging awareness of formal or symmetrical balance in architectural structures but cannot consistently identify them.	The student's public building design shows some awareness of how to use formal or symmetrical balance.	The student attempts to evaluate his or her own work but shows an incomplete understanding of evaluation criteria.
1 POINT	The student cannot demonstrate knowledge of the United States Capitol and Eiffel Tower.	The student cannot identify how formal or symmetrical balance is used in architectural structures.	The student's public building design shows no understanding of how to use formal or symmetrical balance.	The student makes no attempt to evaluate his or her own work.

Level 6 • Unit 4 • Lesson 2

	Art History and Culture	Aesthetic Perception	Creative Expression	Art Criticism
3 POINTS	The student demonstrates knowledge of the lives and work of Georgia O'Keeffe and Ferdinand Hodler.	The student accurately identifies the use of approximate symmetry in two-dimensional works of art.	The student's computer design demonstrates how to use approximate symmetry.	The student thoughtfully and honestly evaluates his or her own work using the four steps of art criticism.
2 POINTS	The student's knowledge of the lives and work of Georgia O'Keeffe and Ferdinand Hodler is weak or incomplete.	The student shows an emerging awareness of approximate symmetry in two-dimensional art but cannot consistently identify it.	The student's computer design shows some awareness of how to use approximate symmetry.	The student attempts to evaluate his or her own work but shows an incomplete understanding of evaluation criteria.
1 POINT	The student cannot demonstrate knowledge of the lives and work of Georgia O'Keeffe and Ferdinand Hodler.	The student cannot identify how approximate symmetry used.	The student's computer design shows no understanding of how to use approximate symmetry.	The student makes no attempt to evaluate his or her own work.

Creative Expression Rubrics

Level 6 • Unit 4 • Lesson 3

	Art History and Culture	Aesthetic Perception	Creative Expression	Art Criticism
3 POINTS	The student demonstrates knowledge of the lives and work of Hokusai and Cassatt.	The student accurately identifies the use of informal or asymmetrical balance in two-dimensional works of art.	The student's still life demonstrates how to use informal or asymmetrical balance.	The student thoughtfully and honestly evaluates his or her own work using the four steps of art criticism.
2 POINTS	The student's knowledge of the lives and work of Hokusai and Cassatt is weak or incomplete.	The student shows an emerging awareness of informal balance in two-dimensional works of art but cannot consistently identify it.	The student's still life shows some awareness of how to use informal or asymmetrical balance.	The student attempts to evaluate his or her own work but shows an incomplete understanding of evaluation criteria.
1 POINT	The student cannot demonstrate knowledge of the lives and work of Hokusai and Cassatt.	The student cannot identify how informal or asymmetrical balance is used in two-dimensional works of art.	The student's still life shows no understanding of how to use informal or asymmetrical balance.	The student makes no attempt to evaluate his or her own work.

Level 6 • Unit 4 • Lesson 4

	Art History and Culture	Aesthetic Perception	Creative Expression	Art Criticism
3 POINTS	The student demonstrates knowledge of *Bull's Eye Quilt* and the soul discs.	The student accurately identifies the use of radial balance in a variety of works of art.	The student's radial design demonstrates how to use radial balance.	The student thoughtfully and honestly evaluates his or her own work using the four steps of art criticism.
2 POINTS	The student's knowledge of *Bull's Eye Quilt* and the soul discs is weak or incomplete.	The student shows an emerging awareness of radial balance in a variety of works of art but cannot consistently identify them.	The student's radial design shows some awareness of how to use radial balance.	The student attempts to evaluate his or her own work but shows an incomplete understanding of evaluation criteria.
1 POINT	The student cannot demonstrate knowledge of *Bull's Eye Quilt* and the soul discs.	The student cannot identify how radial balance is used in an artwork.	The student's radial design shows no understanding of how to use radial balance.	The student makes no attempt to evaluate his or her own work.

Creative Expression Rubrics

Level 6 • Unit 4 • Lesson 5

	Art History and Culture	Aesthetic Perception	Creative Expression	Art Criticism
3 POINTS	The student demonstrates knowledge of the lives and work of Sharp and Rothenberg.	The student accurately identifies the use of emphasis in two-dimensional works of art.	The student's collograph print demonstrates an understanding of how to use an art element to create emphasis.	The student thoughtfully and honestly evaluates his or her own work using the four steps of art criticism.
2 POINTS	The student's knowledge of the lives and work of Sharp and Rothenberg is weak or incomplete.	The student shows an emerging awareness of how emphasis is used in two-dimensional works of art but cannot consistently identify it.	The student's collograph print shows some awareness of how to create emphasis using an art element.	The student attempts to evaluate his or her own work but shows an incomplete understanding of evaluation criteria.
1 POINT	The student cannot demonstrate knowledge of the lives and work of Sharp and Rothenberg.	The student cannot identify how emphasis is used.	The student's collograph print shows no understanding of how to create emphasis.	The student makes no attempt to evaluate his or her own work.

Level 6 • Unit 4 • Lesson 6

	Art History and Culture	Aesthetic Perception	Creative Expression	Art Criticism
3 POINTS	The student demonstrates knowledge of the lives and works of Segal and Muñoz.	The student accurately identifies the use of emphasis in an arrangement of three-dimensional objects.	The student's group sculpture demonstrates using emphasis of an area.	The student thoughtfully and honestly evaluates his or her own work using the four steps of art criticism.
2 POINTS	The student's knowledge of the lives and works of Segal and Muñoz is weak or incomplete.	The student shows an emerging awareness of emphasis in three-dimensional objects but cannot consistently identify it.	The student's group sculpture shows some awareness of emphasis of an area.	The student attempts to evaluate his or her own work but shows an incomplete understanding of evaluation criteria.
1 POINT	The student cannot demonstrate knowledge of the lives and works of Segal and Muñoz.	The student cannot identify how emphasis of an area is created.	The student's group sculpture shows no understanding of how to use emphasis of an area.	The student makes no attempt to evaluate his or her own work.

Creative Expression Rubrics

Level 6 • Unit 5 • Lesson 1

	Art History and Culture	Aesthetic Perception	Creative Expression	Art Criticism
3 POINTS	The student demonstrates knowledge of the lives and work of Bishop and Copley.	The student accurately identifies the use of facial proportion in portraits.	The student's self-portrait demonstrates use of facial proportions.	The student thoughtfully and honestly evaluates his or her own work using the four steps of art criticism.
2 POINTS	The student's knowledge of the lives and work of Bishop and Copley is weak or incomplete.	The student shows an emerging awareness of facial proportion in portraits but cannot consistently identify it.	The student's self-portrait shows some awareness of how to use facial proportions.	The student attempts to evaluate his or her own work but shows an incomplete understanding of evaluation criteria.
1 POINT	The student cannot demonstrate knowledge of the lives and work of Bishop and Copley.	The student cannot identify how facial proportions are used in portraits.	The student's self-portrait shows no understanding of how to use facial proportions.	The student makes no attempt to evaluate his or her own work.

Level 6 • Unit 5 • Lesson 2

	Art History and Culture	Aesthetic Perception	Creative Expression	Art Criticism
3 POINTS	The student demonstrates knowledge of *Armor of George Clifford* and *Dancing Lady*.	The student accurately identifies the use of figure proportion in various works of art.	The student's figure drawing demonstrates how to use figure proportion.	The student thoughtfully and honestly evaluates his or her own work using the four steps of art criticism.
2 POINTS	The student's knowledge of *Armor of George Clifford* and *Dancing Lady* is weak or incomplete.	The student shows an emerging awareness of figure proportion in various works of art but cannot consistently identify it.	The student's figure drawing shows some awareness of how to use figure proportion.	The student attempts to evaluate his or her own work but shows an incomplete understanding of evaluation criteria.
1 POINT	The student cannot demonstrate knowledge of *Armor of George Clifford* and *Dancing Lady*.	The student cannot identify how figure proportion is used in any works of art.	The student's figure drawing shows no understanding of how to use figure proportion.	The student makes no attempt to evaluate his or her own work.

Creative Expression Rubrics

Level 6 • Unit 5 • Lesson 3

	Art History and Culture	Aesthetic Perception	Creative Expression	Art Criticism
3 POINTS	The student demonstrates knowledge of Edvard Munch and face jugs.	The student accurately identifies the use of facial distortion in two- and three-dimensional works of art.	The student's face jug demonstrates how to use facial distortion.	The student thoughtfully and honestly evaluates his or her own work using the four steps of art criticism.
2 POINTS	The student's knowledge of Edvard Munch and face jugs is weak or incomplete.	The student shows an emerging awareness of facial distortion in two- and three-dimensional works of art but cannot consistently identify it.	The student's face jug shows some awareness of how to use facial distortion.	The student attempts to evaluate his or her own work but shows an incomplete understanding of evaluation criteria.
1 POINT	The student cannot demonstrate knowledge of Edvard Munch and face jugs.	The student cannot identify how facial distortion is used in two- or three-dimensional works of art.	The student's face jug shows no understanding of how to use facial distortion.	The student makes no attempt to evaluate his or her own work.

Level 6 • Unit 5 • Lesson 4

	Art History and Culture	Aesthetic Perception	Creative Expression	Art Criticism
3 POINTS	The student demonstrates knowledge of the lives and work of Giacometti and Botero.	The student accurately identifies the use of figure distortion in a variety of works of art.	The student's artwork demonstrates how to use figure distortion.	The student thoughtfully and honestly evaluates his or her own work using the four steps of art criticism.
2 POINTS	The student's knowledge of the lives and work of Giacometti and Botero is weak or incomplete.	The student shows an emerging awareness of figure distortion in a variety of works of art but cannot consistently identify it.	The student's artwork shows some awareness of how to use figure distortion.	The student attempts to evaluate his or her own work but shows an incomplete understanding of evaluation criteria.
1 POINT	The student cannot demonstrate knowledge of the lives and work of Giacometti or Botero.	The student cannot identify how figure distortion is used in an artwork.	The student's artwork shows no understanding of how to use figure distortion.	The student makes no attempt to evaluate his or her own work.

Creative Expression Rubrics

Level 6 • Unit 5 • Lesson 5

	Art History and Culture	Aesthetic Perception	Creative Expression	Art Criticism
3 POINTS	The student demonstrates knowledge of the lives and work of Safdie and Russell.	The student accurately identifies the use of realistic scale in three-dimensional works of art.	The student's chair design demonstrates how to use realistic scale.	The student thoughtfully and honestly evaluates his or her own work using the four steps of art criticism.
2 POINTS	The student's knowledge of the lives and work of Safdie and Russell is weak or incomplete.	The student shows an emerging awareness of realistic scale in three-dimensional works of art but cannot consistently identify it.	The student's chair design shows some awareness of how to use realistic scale.	The student attempts to evaluate his or her own work but shows an incomplete understanding of evaluation criteria.
1 POINT	The student cannot demonstrate knowledge of the lives and work of Safdie or Russell.	The student cannot identify how realistic scale is used in an artwork.	The student's chair design shows no understanding of how to use realistic scale.	The student makes no attempt to evaluate his or her own work.

Level 6 • Unit 5 • Lesson 6

	Art History and Culture	Aesthetic Perception	Creative Expression	Art Criticism
3 POINTS	The student demonstrates knowledge of the lives and work of Picasso and Dalí.	The student accurately identifies the use of unrealistic scale in a variety of works of art.	The student's surreal landscape collage demonstrates how to use unrealistic scale.	The student thoughtfully and honestly evaluates his or her own work using the four steps of art criticism.
2 POINTS	The student's knowledge of the lives and work of Picasso and Dalí is weak or incomplete.	The student shows an emerging awareness of unrealistic scale in a variety of works of art but cannot consistently identify it.	The student's surreal landscape collage shows some awareness of how to use unrealistic scale.	The student attempts to evaluate his or her own work but shows an incomplete understanding of evaluation criteria.
1 POINT	The student cannot demonstrate knowledge of the lives and work of Picasso or Dalí.	The student cannot identify how unrealistic scale is used in an artwork.	The student's surreal landscape collage shows no understanding of how to use unrealistic scale.	The student makes no attempt to evaluate his or her own work.

Creative Expression Rubrics

Level 6 • Unit 6 • Lesson 1

Art History and Culture	Aesthetic Perception	Creative Expression	Art Criticism
3 POINTS The student demonstrates knowledge of the lives and work of Bustion and Bennion.	The student accurately identifies the use of variety through line, shape, and color in two-dimensional works of art.	The student's collage demonstrates how to create variety through line, shape, and color.	The student thoughtfully and honestly evaluates his or her own work using the four steps of art criticism.
2 POINTS The student's knowledge of the lives and work of Bustion and Bennion is weak or incomplete.	The student shows an emerging awareness of the use of variety through line, shape, and color but cannot consistently identify it.	The student's collage shows some awareness of how to create variety through line, shape, and color.	The student attempts to evaluate his or her own work but shows an incomplete understanding of evaluation criteria.
1 POINT The student cannot demonstrate knowledge of the lives and work of Bustion or Bennion.	The student cannot identify how variety through line, shape, and color is used in an artwork.	The student's collage shows no understanding of how to create variety through line, shape, and color.	The student makes no attempt to evaluate his or her own work.

Level 6 • Unit 6 • Lesson 2

Art History and Culture	Aesthetic Perception	Creative Expression	Art Criticism
3 POINTS The student demonstrates knowledge of the lives and work of Ragans and Brach.	The student accurately identifies the use of variety through contrast of value in two-dimensional works of art.	The student's hand-colored photograph demonstrates variety through contrast of value.	The student thoughtfully and honestly evaluates his or her own work using the four steps of art criticism.
2 POINTS The student's knowledge of the lives and work of Ragans and Brach is weak or incomplete.	The student shows an emerging awareness of variety through contrast of value but cannot consistently identify it.	The student's hand-colored photograph shows some awareness of variety through contrast of value.	The student attempts to evaluate his or her own work but shows an incomplete understanding of evaluation criteria.
1 POINT The student cannot demonstrate knowledge of the lives and work of Ragans or Brach.	The student cannot identify how variety through contrast of value is used in an artwork.	The student's hand-colored photograph shows no understanding of variety through contrast of value.	The student makes no attempt to evaluate his or her own work.

Creative Expression Rubrics

Level 6 • Unit 6 • Lesson 3

	Art History and Culture	Aesthetic Perception	Creative Expression	Art Criticism
3 POINTS	The student demonstrates knowledge of Grandma Moses and Guatemalan culture.	The student accurately identifies the use of harmony in two-dimensional decorations.	The student's embroidery piece demonstrates harmony in two-dimensional decoration.	The student thoughtfully and honestly evaluates his or her own work using the four steps of art criticism.
2 POINTS	The student's knowledge of Grandma Moses and Guatemalan culture is weak or incomplete.	The student shows an emerging awareness of harmony in two-dimensional decorations but cannot consistently identify it.	The student's embroidery piece shows some awareness of harmony in two-dimensional decoration.	The student attempts to evaluate his or her own work but shows an incomplete understanding of evaluation criteria.
1 POINT	The student cannot demonstrate knowledge of Grandma Moses or Guatemalan culture.	The student cannot identify how harmony is used in an artwork.	The student's embroidery piece shows no understanding of harmony in two-dimensional decoration.	The student makes no attempt to evaluate his or her own work.

Level 6 • Unit 6 • Lesson 4

	Art History and Culture	Aesthetic Perception	Creative Expression	Art Criticism
3 POINTS	The student demonstrates knowledge of the lives and work of Nevelson and Ellett.	The student accurately identifies the use of harmony in sculpture.	The student's assemblage demonstrates harmony in sculpture.	The student thoughtfully and honestly evaluates his or her own work using the four steps of art criticism.
2 POINTS	The student's knowledge of the lives and work of Nevelson and Ellett is weak or incomplete.	The student shows an emerging awareness of harmony in sculpture but cannot consistently identify it.	The student's assemblage shows some awareness of harmony.	The student attempts to evaluate his or her own work but shows an incomplete understanding of evaluation criteria.
1 POINT	The student cannot demonstrate knowledge of the lives and work of Nevelson and Ellett.	The student cannot identify how harmony is used in an artwork.	The student's assemblage shows no understanding of harmony.	The student makes no attempt to evaluate his or her own work.

Creative Expression Rubrics

Level 6 • Unit 6 • Lesson 5

	Art History and Culture	Aesthetic Perception	Creative Expression	Art Criticism
3 POINTS	The student demonstrates knowledge of Keyser and Indonesian culture.	The student accurately identifies the use of unity in a weaving.	The student's weaving demonstrates unity.	The student thoughtfully and honestly evaluates his or her own work using the four steps of art criticism.
2 POINTS	The student's knowledge of the Keyser and Indonesian culture is weak or incomplete.	The student shows an emerging awareness of unity in a weaving but cannot consistently identify it.	The student's weaving shows some awareness of unity.	The student attempts to evaluate his or her own work but shows an incomplete understanding of evaluation criteria.
1 POINT	The student cannot demonstrate knowledge of Keyser or Indonesian culture.	The student cannot identify how unity is used in a weaving.	The student's weaving shows no understanding of unity.	The student makes no attempt to evaluate his or her own work.

Level 6 • Unit 6 • Lesson 6

	Art History and Culture	Aesthetic Perception	Creative Expression	Art Criticism
3 POINTS	The student demonstrates knowledge of the lives and work of Paik and Lemon.	The student accurately identifies the use of unity in three-dimensional art.	The student's sculpture demonstrates unity.	The student thoughtfully and honestly evaluates his or her own work using the four steps of art criticism.
2 POINTS	The student's knowledge of the lives and work of Paik and Lemon is weak or incomplete.	The student shows an emerging awareness of unity in three-dimensional art but cannot consistently identify it.	The student's sculpture shows some awareness of unity.	The student attempts to evaluate his or her own work but shows an incomplete understanding of evaluation criteria.
1 POINT	The student cannot demonstrate knowledge of the lives and work of Paik or Lemon.	The student cannot identify how unity is used in three-dimensional art.	The student's sculpture shows no understanding of unity.	The student makes no attempt to evaluate his or her own work.